ACKNOWLEDGEMENTS

The publishers would like to thank the following sources for permission to reproduce illustrations: E.T. ARCHIVE: pp.28, 29, 83; MARY EVANS PICTURE LIBRARY: pp.14, 80; FINE ART PHOTOGRAPHIC LIBRARY: pp.6–7, 8, 11, 17, 18, 20, 22, 25, 26, 31, 34, 36, 39, 40, 41, 43, 44, 46, 49, 51, 52, 55T, 58, 60, 62B, 63, 65, 68, 71, 72, 75, 77, 78, 81, 85, 86, 89, 92, 94, 98, 99, 101, 102, 105, 109

The publishers also wish to acknowledge the following sources for quotations:
IRISH PROVERBS by Laurence Flanagan (Gill & Macmillan, Dublin);
DUBLIN TENEMENT LIFE, AN ORAL HISTORY by Kevin C. Kearns (Gill & Macmillan, Dublin);
THE LADY POETS, AN ANTHOLOGY selected by Joan Forman (Jarrold Publishing, Norwich);
LIKE A FISH NEEDS A BICYCLE AND OVER 3,000 QUOTATIONS BY AND ABOUT WOMEN edited by Anne Stibbs (Bloomsbury Publishing, London);
PILLARS OF THE HOUSE, AN ANTHOLOGY OF VERSE BY IRISH WOMEN FROM 1690 TO THE PRESENT edited by A.A. Kelly (Wolfhound Press, Dublin);
THE COMPLETE LETTERS OF LADY MARY WORTLEY MONTAGU edited by R. Halsband (Clarendon Press, London);
LOVE'S WITNESS FIVE CENTURIES OF LOVE POETRY BY WOMEN compiled by Jill Hollis (Robinson, London);
JOURNAL TO STELLA by Jonathan Swift (J.M. Dent & Sons, London);
AUTOBIOGRAPHY AND CORRESPONDENCE OF MARY GRANVILLE, MRS. DELANY edited by Lady Llanover;
ENQUIRE WITHIN UPON EVERYTHING (Madgwick, Houlston, London); POEMS by Denis Florence MacCarthy (M.H. Gill, Dublin);
VOICES ON THE WIND WOMEN POETS OF THE CELTIC TWILIGHT edited by Eilís Ní Dhuibhne (New Island Books, Dublin);
FAVOURITE POEMS WE LEARNED IN SCHOOL edited by Thomas F. Walsh (Mercier Press, Cork);
BETWEEN INNOCENCE AND PEACE FAVOURITE POEMS OF IRELAND edited by Brendan Kennelly (Mercier Press, Cork);
LETTERS AND ESSAYS, MORAL AND MISCELLANEOUS by M. Hays; JOURNAL OF A LADY OF FASHION by Marguerite, Countess of Blessington;
RETROSPECTIONS OF DOROTHEA HERBERT by Dorothea Herbert;
A SOLDIER'S WIFE, AN AUTOBIOGRAPHY by Lady Elizabeth Butler;
CASTLE RACKRENT by Maria Edgeworth (J.M. Dent & Sons, London);
THE ABSENTEE by Maria Edgeworth (J.M. Dent & Sons, London);
A LITTLE IRISH GIRL by J.M. Callwell;
FLORENCE MACARTHY by Lady Morgan;
RE-ECHOES by Frances Power Cobbe;
THE IRISH COUNTRY HOUSE, A SOCIAL HISTORY by Peter Somerville-Large (Sinclair Stevenson, London);
ANCIENT LEGENDS OF IRELAND by Lady Jane Francesca Wilde (Speranza);
CONSTANCE MARKIEVICZ by A. Haverty (Pandora Press, London)

Edited by FLEUR ROBERTSON

Designed by SARAH STANLEY AND HEATHER BLAGDON

Picture Research by FELICITY COX

Production by RUTH ARTHUR, KAREN STAFF, NEIL RANDLES

Director of Production GERALD HUGHES

Published in Ireland by
Gill & Macmillan Ltd, Goldenbridge, Dublin 8
and associated companies around the world

Ref 16285
This selection
© 1997 by Waverley 1770, Godalming, Surrey
ISBN 0 7171 2618 8

PREVIOUS PAGE: *Dreaming*, CHECA Y SANZ, ULPIANO (1860–1916)

A GIFT FOR

. . . .

FROM

. . . .

GILL & MACMILLAN

An Irish Woman's Book of Days

—Days—

INSPIRATION

AND

CELEBRATION

'And what can the thousands upon thousands do for me? Hearts, you know, Lady Anne, are to be won only by radiant eyes.'

MARIA EDGEWORTH

---- ·≈ 1 ≈· ----

1800 *Birth of Maria Edgeworth, Irish author best known for* Castle Rackrent
1800 *Birth of Gretta Bowen, Irish artist*

---- ·≈ 2 ≈· ----

Songs of our land, ye are with us forever
FRANCES BROWNE

---- ·≈ 3 ≈· ----

1925 *Birth of Maureen Potter, Irish actress and comedienne*

---- ·≈ 4 ≈· ----

'Where the red wine-cup floweth, there art thou!'
CAROLINE NORTON

---- ·≈ 5 ≈· ----

1826 *Separate Irish currency abolished and replaced by sterling*

---- ·≈ 6 ≈· ----

1800 *Birth of Anna Maria Hall, Irish novelist, travel writer and philanthropist*
1794 *Birth of Frances Ball (Mother Mary Theresa), Irish founder of the Sisters of Loreto*

---- ·≈ 7 ≈· ----

'And all the young ladies … said … that to be sure a love match was the only thing for
happiness where the parties could any way afford it.'
from *Castle Rackrent*, MARIA EDGEWORTH

*H*ere, my dear Aunt, I
was interrupted in a
manner that will surprise you as
much as it surprised me, by the
coming in of Monsieur
Edelcrantz, a Swedish
gentleman, whom we have
mentioned to you, of superior
understanding and mild
manners; he came to offer me
his hand and heart!!

MARIA EDGEWORTH
writing to her aunt,
Paris, 1802. She was
to remain unmarried.

✤ 8 ✤

1779 *Birth of Julia Glover, Irish actress*
1926 *Birth of Iris Kellett, Irish international showjumper*

✤ 9 ✤

1594 *Trinity College Dublin, Ireland's first university, opens its gates to students*

✤ 10 ✤

You'll live during the year, for we were just talking of you
TRADITIONAL PROVERB

✤ 11 ✤

1935 *American Amelia Earhart becomes the first woman to make a solo flight across the Pacific Ocean*

✤ 12 ✤

1930 *Birth of Jennifer Johnston, Irish author*
1887 *Birth of Máire O'Neill (Molly Allgood) Irish actress and fiancée of J.M. Synge*

✤ 13 ✤

Home was home then and the people friendly
KATHARINE TYNAN

✤ 14 ✤

A good heart never went to hell
IRISH PROVERB

The grey mornings I well remember,
The grey mountains new-waked from slumber,
The grey dews on the trees and hedges,
And in grey distance the grey sea's edges.

from *The Grey Mornings*
KATHARINE TYNAN

I'm Irish, you know, it all comes of that', Norah would say modestly when complimented on her fertility of invention. There was nothing indeed of which she was so proud as her Irish name and her Irish descent, although she herself had never set foot in Ireland …

from
A Little Irish Girl
J.M. CALLWELL

A Labour of Love, WILLIAM M. HAY (FL. 1852–1881)

15

1860 *Birth of Eleanor Hull, Irish author, folklorist and Celtic scholar*

*Who takes the child by
the hand takes
the mother by the heart*

TRADITIONAL
PROVERB

16

1816 *Birth of Frances Browne, Irish poet and children's storyteller*

17

*First woman: Whenever I'm down in the dumps, I get myself another hat.
Second woman: I always wondered where you found them.*

ANON.

❖ 18 ❖

1822 *Theatre Royal in Hawkins Street, Dublin, opens*

❖ 19 ❖

1787 *Birth of Mary Aikenhead, founder of the Irish Sisters of Charity and*
St Vincent's Hospital, Dublin

❖ 20 ❖

1926 *Birth of Patricia Neal, Oscar-winning American film actress*
1908 *Opening of the Municipal Gallery of Modern Art, later named for Hugh Lane,*
Parnell Square, Dublin

❖ 21 ❖

1894 *Birth of Theresa Davy, Irish playwright*
1861 *Birth of Katharine Tynan, Irish poet and journalist*

❖ THE IRISH MANNER ❖

I wish you could see the sort of comfort all these families have in one
another, you would then think of a large family as a blessing. I must
admire the Irish manner of bringing up children, for in all the families I
have happened to know there seems the most perfect ease and confidence, and
except for their attention to each other you would never find out which were
fathers and mothers and which were daughters … even the Duke of Leinster, where
there is a good deal of state, I could not help admiring the great grown up girls stealing an
opportunity when they thought the company did not mind them to go to their father and
mother with an appearance of affection that did them good. I will adopt this comfortable
fashion if I can with my own children in spite of the vulgarity of it, for I am convinced
familiarity with one's children is looked upon in that light by a great many of the English.

LADY CAROLINE DAWSON *from Ireland to her sister in London, 1776*

Florence Nightingale at Sartari, ANONYMOUS (C. 1854)

JANUARY

22
1967 *Birth of Eleanor McEvoy, Irish singer-songwriter*

23
1834 *Opening of St Vincent's Hospital, Dublin*

24
1862 *Birth of Edith Wharton, American novelist*

25
No one can make you feel inferior without your consent
ELEANOR ROOSEVELT

26
1928 *Birth of Eartha Kitt, American singer and actress*

27
1944 *Birth of Mairead Corrigan-Maguire, Irish co-founder of the Peace People*

28
I do not love thee! – no! I do not love thee!
And yet when thou are absent I am sad …
from *I Do Not Love Thee*, CAROLINE NORTON

There is no sea so deep, my
own, no mountain so high,
That I should not come to
you if I heard you cry.

There is no hell so sunken,
no heaven so steep,
Where I should not seek my
own, find you and keep.

from *Maternity*
KATHARINE TYNAN

Much enjoyment, and in some cases great benefit, might be obtained, at very little trouble or expense, if a few congenial friends arranged to meet once a week for reading, discussion, music, games, or any other amusement mutually agreed upon.

from *Social Evenings*
19th century women's
magazine article

29

1939 *Birth of Germaine Greer, Australian author and feminist*

30

1845 *Birth of Katharine Wood, better known as Kitty O'Shea,*
English mistress and later wife of Irish leader Charles Stewart Parnell

31

1864 *Birth of Matilda Knowles, internationally respected Irish botanist*
1885 *Birth of Anna Pavlova, Russian prima ballerina*

O had you seen the Coolun

Walking down by the cuckoo's street,

With the dew of the meadow shining

On her milk-white twinkling feet!

My love she is, and my colleen oge,

And she dwells in Bal'nagar;

And she bears the palm of beauty bright

From the fairest that in Erin are.

from *The Coolun*, trans. SAMUEL FERGUSON

Hugging the Old Illusion warm and dear,
The Silence and the Wise Book and the Lamp.
EVA GORE-BOOTH

La Belle Dame Sans Merci, WALTER CRANE (1845–1915)

An Irish Woman's

FEBRUARY

We are the gentle people:
The passing dust we are,
With gusty laughter blowing
    Near and far.
We are the gentle people,
Nor deal in praise or blame,
But we stand before your sorrow,
And we stand behind your shame.

NORA HOPPER CHESSON

FEBRUARY

1

1982 *Ban on corporal punishment in Republic of Ireland schools came into effect*

2

1650 *Birth of Nell Gwyn, British actress and royal mistress*

3

1896 *Death of Lady Jane Wilde, Irish author who wrote under the pen name 'Speranza'*

4

1865 *Birth of Maud Gonne MacBride, Irish revolutionary and republican campaigner*
1868 *Birth of Constance Markievicz, Irish revolutionary*

5

1829 *Coombe Lying-in Hospital opens in Dublin*
1921 *Death of Katharine (Kitty) O'Shea, wife of Irish leader Charles Stewart Parnell*

6

Rain in February is as good as manure
TRADITIONAL PROVERB

7

1924 *Birth of Dora Bryan, British comedy actress*

LEFT: *Fair Rosamund and Queen Eleanor*, SIR EDWARD COLEY BURNE-JONES (1833–1898)

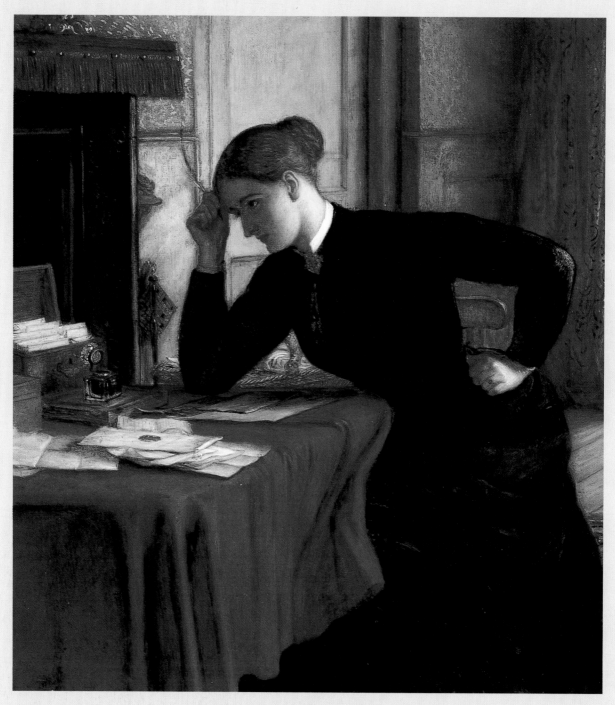

Faraway Thoughts, CHARLES WEST COPE (1811–1890)

FEBRUARY

Persons who are accustomed to use tea-leaves for sweeping their carpets, and find that they leave stains, will do well to employ fresh-cut grass instead. It is better than tea-leaves for preventing dust, and gives the carpets a very bright fresh look.

Sweeping Carpets
magazine article c. 1910

8

1926 *First performance of Sean O'Casey's* The Plough and the Stars *at the Abbey Theatre, Dublin, leads to rioting three nights later*

9

Triur gan riaghal – bean, múile agus muc
IRISH PROVERB

10

1818 *Death of Lady Eleanor Palmer, noted Irish beauty*

11

1984 *Closure of Royal Hibernian Hotel, Dublin*

12

1934 *Birth of Mary Quant, British fashion designer*

13

1827 *Birth of Sister Julia McGroarty, Irish founder of Trinity College, Washington D.C.*

14

1853 *The* Queen Victoria *sinks in a snowstorm off Howth Head. Fifty-five lives lost.*

Over the dim blue hills
Strays a wild river,
Over the dim blue hills
Rests my heart ever.
Dearer and brighter than
Jewels and pearl,
Dwells she in beauty
there
Máire my girl.

JOHN KEEGAN CASEY

Flower Arrangement (Teatime), SYDNEY MUSCHAMP (fl. 1884–1904)

FEBRUARY

> *W*omen were the providers, it was always the women. The fathers were there but they seemed invisible. The women were the mainstay, they were everything. They were mother, father, counsellor, doctor … everything. An awful lot of saints.
>
> UNA SHAW
> *Dublin tenement resident*

15

1971 *Decimal day: Irish currency officially changed over to the decimal system*

16

She's descended from a long line her mother listened to.
GYPSY ROSE LEE

17

1944 *Birth of Brenda Fricker, Oscar-winning Irish actress*
1980 *The Derrynaflan Chalice and other ancient treasure discovered in Co. Tipperary*

18

1931 *Birth of Toni Morrison, American author*

19

1911 *Birth of Merle Oberon (Estelle Marie O'Brien Thompson), Tasmanian film actress*

20

I am righteously indignant, you are annoyed, she is making a fuss about nothing
ANON.

21

'Shut up!' Mother explained
ANON.

> *Some hours we should find for the pleasures of the mind*
> VICTORIAN PROVERB

❧ 22 ❧

1832 *First burial in Glasnevin Cemetery, Dublin*

❧ 23 ❧

1943 *Thirty-five orphan girls die in a fire at St Joseph's Orphanage, Cavan town*

❧ 24 ❧

1920 *Nancy Astor becomes the first woman to speak in the House of Commons*

❧ 25 ❧

1890 *Birth of Dame Myra Hess, British concert pianist*

❧ 26 ❧

One good turn gets most of the blanket
OLD SAYING

❧ 27 ❧

Fiadhnaise a' ghiolla bhréagaigh a bhean
IRISH PROVERB

❧ 28/29 ❧

1938 *Birth of Alice Taylor, Irish author (28th)*

*When I was young the days
were long,
Oh, long the days when I
was young:
So long from morn to evenfall
As they would never end
at all.*

from The Flying Wheel
KATHARINE TYNAN

But it is especially in the treatment of women by men that chivalry is always supposed to show itself. How may this be with us now? We fear it is a very enigmatical thing, this same masculine chivalry of the nineteenth century. In the humbler ranks it never induces men to prevent women from doing the hardest and coarsest labour. They may sweep crossings and fill coal trucks … and no chivalry says 'Leave it for me!'

FRANCES POWER COBBE

Fantasia in White, ALBERT LUDOVICI (1820–1894)

An Irish Woman's

MARCH

Some say he's dark,
I say he's bonny,
He's the flower of them all
My handsome, coaxing Johnny.

I know where I'm going,
I know who's going with me,
I know who I love,
But the dear knows who I'll marry.

TRADITIONAL SONG

⚜ 1 ⚜

1905 *Birth of Nano Reid, Irish artist*
1942 *Birth of Aine Hyland, Irish educationalist*

⚜ 2 ⚜

1950 *Birth of Karen Carpenter, American singer*

⚜ 3 ⚜

1854 *Death of Harriet Smithson, Irish actress who*
captivated the composer Hector Berlioz

Do good to your enemy, that he may become your friend. Do good to your friend, that he remain your friend.

ANON.

⚜ 4 ⚜

It's the jewel that can't be got that is the most beautiful
TRADITIONAL PROVERB

⚜ 5 ⚜

Would but indulgent Fortune send
To me a kind, and faithful friend
MARY CHUDLEIGH

⚜ 6 ⚜

1944 *Birth of Dame Kiri Te Kanawa, New Zealand opera singer*

Nothing ever was half so tiresome as musical parties: no one gives them except those who can exhibit themselves, and fancy they excel …: except that all the world of fashion are there, I would never go to another; for, positively, it is ten times more fatiguing than staying at home. To be compelled to look charmed, and to applaud, when you are half-dead from suppressing yawns, and to see half-a-dozen very tolerable men, with whom one could have a very pleasant chat, except for the stupid music, is really too bad.

from *Journal of a Lady of Fashion*
THE COUNTESS OF BLESSINGTON

LEFT: *Pink Blossom*, HAROLD H. PIFFARD (fl. 1895–1899)

MARCH

7

1920 *Birth of Eilis Dillon, Irish novelist best known for* Across the Bitter Sea
1736 *Birth of Marie-Louise O'Morphi, Irish courtesan, mistress of King Louis XV of France*

8

1770 *Birth of Mary Ann McCracken, lover of Thomas Russell,*
'The Man From God Knows Where'

9

The more I see of men, the better I like dogs
MME ROLAND

10

Nobility listens to art
IRISH PROVERB

La Primavera,
detail of *Spring,* SANDRO
BOTTICELLI
(1445–1510)

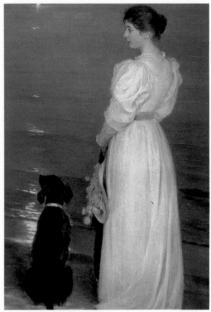

*Summer Evening at Skagen, the Artist's Wife
with a Dog on a Beach*
PETER SEVERIN KROYER (1851-1909)

✣ 11 ✣

*1953 Birth of Mary Harney, Irish politician, the first woman
to lead a party in Dáil Éireann*

✣ 12 ✣

1946 Birth of Liza Minnelli, American actress and singer

> *One half of the world
> cannot understand the
> pleasures of the other.*
>
> JANE AUSTEN

✣ 13 ✣

General notions are generally wrong
LADY MARY WORTLEY MONTAGU

14
1985 *Two schoolchildren in Asdee, Co. Kerry, report
that the local Marian statue had 'moved'*

15
1852 *Birth of Lady Gregory, Irish playwright, author
and co-founder of Dublin's Abbey Theatre*

16
1896 *First use of X-rays in Ireland, at Dr Steevens's Hospital, Dublin*

> *The little waves of
> Breffny go stumbling
> through my soul.*
>
> EVA GORE-BOOTH

17
Saint Patrick's Day
1864 *Birth of Charlotte Milligan Fox, folk music collector and author*

18
1956 *Marriage of Prince Rainier of Monaco and
Grace Kelly, Irish-American film actress*

19
The beauty of a chaste woman makes bitter words
IRISH PROVERB

A Lady of Leisure, FREDERIC SOULACROIX (1825–1879)

⋅ 20 ⋅

1872 *Birth of Karin Michaelis, Danish author and feminist*

⋅ 21 ⋅

1970 *Dana brings Ireland victory in the Eurovision Song Contest for the first time*
1884 *Birth of Nora Barnacle, wife of the novelist James Joyce*

⋅ 22 ⋅

1848 *Birth of Sarah Purser, Irish artist*
1768 *Birth of Melasina Trench, Irish author*

⋅ 23 ⋅

1908 *Birth of Joan Crawford, American film actress and dancer*

⋅ 24 ⋅

1968 *Tuskar Rock air-disaster, Co. Wexford. Sixty-one killed.*

---

*Hope is the thing with
feathers
That perches in the soul
And sings the tune
without the words
And never stops at all.*

EMILY DICKINSON

⋅ 25 ⋅

Ní'l nídh níos géire 'na teanga mná
IRISH PROVERB

⋅ 26 ⋅

1944 *Birth of Diana Ross, American actress and singer*

MARCH

❧ 27 ❧

1872 Birth of Mary MacSwiney, Irish republican

❧ 28 ❧

1686 First pensioners admitted to the Royal Hospital, Kilmainham
1824 Death of Catherine Wilmot, Irish traveller and diarist

❧ 29 ❧

1873 Birth of Peig Sayers, renowned storyteller
1793 Death of Charlotte Brooke, author and Ulster folksong collector

---

❧ 30 ❧

Want is the mistress of invention
MRS CENTLIVRE

❧ 31 ❧

A misty winter brings a pleasant spring,
a pleasant winter, a misty spring.
TRADITIONAL RHYME

Kathleen mavourneen, the
gray dawn is breaking
The horn of the hunter is
heard on the hill,
The lark from her light
wing the bright dew is
shaking —
Kathleen mavourneen,
what, slumbering still?
Oh hast thou forgotten
how soon we must sever?
Oh hast thou forgotten this
day we must part?
It may be for years, it
may be forever;
Oh why art thou silent,
thou voice of my heart?

LOUISA CRAWFORD

An Irish Woman's

APRIL

*Believe me, comedy goes through
the world better than tragedy, and,
take it all in all, does rather
less mischief.*

MARIA EDGEWORTH

1
1911 *Launch of the Titanic from Harland & Wolff shipyard, Belfast*

2
1902 *The first production of Yeats' Cathleen ni Houlihan, starring Maud Gonne*
1861 *Death of Katharine Tynan, Irish writer and poet*

3
1900 *Oldest surviving moving film in Ireland shows*
Queen Victoria's last visit to Dublin

4
1917 *Birth of Sheila Conroy, Irish trade unionist*
1951 *Birth of Twink (Adele King), popular singer and actress*

5
1869 *Birth of Margaret Tennant, Irish social work pioneer*

6
May we have the grace of God and may we die in Ireland
IRISH BLESSING

7
1915 *Birth of Billie Holiday, American jazz and blues singer*

Among the innocent recreations of the fireside, there are few more commendable and practicable than those afforded by what are severally termed Enigmas and Charades etc. Of these there are such a variety, that they are suited to every capacity; and they present this additional attraction, that ingenuity may be exercised in the invention of them, as well as their solution. Many persons who have become noted for their literary compositions may date the origin of their success to the time when they attempted the composition of a trifling enigma or charade.

Evening Pastimes
Victorian magazine

Stella and Flavia every hour
Unnumbered hearts surprise;
In Stella's soul lies all her
power,
And Flavia's in her eyes.

MARY BARBER

LEFT: *Going Down Stream*, DAVID WOODLOCK (1842–1929)

Amaryllis, or The Shepherdess, WILLIAM HOLMAN HUNT (1827–1910)

APRIL

8

Gach nidh daor mian gach mnaoi

IRISH PROVERB

9

1984 *Death of Leslie de Barra, Irish revolutionary and Red Cross official*

10

1940 *Birth of Gloria Hunniford, Irish broadcaster*

11

Love against Time: and Love hath won the race

ROSA MULHOLLAND

12

1737 *Margaret ('Peg') Woffington, Irish actress, plays Ophelia, her first serious role, at Smock Alley Theatre, Dublin*

13

1742 *Premiere of Handel's* Messiah *in Dublin*
1953 *Death of Alice Milligan, Irish poet and cultural revivalist*

Yes'm, old friends is always best, 'less you can catch a new one that's fit to make an old one out of!

SARAH ORNE JEWETT

14

1859 *Death of Lady Sydney Owenson Morgan, Irish novelist and activist in the cause of Catholic Emancipation*

APRIL

❧ 15 ❧

1882 *Birth of Mary Swanzy, Irish painter*
1912 *The luxury liner Titanic sinks off Newfoundland; of the 1500 who perish, 187 are Irish*

❧ 16 ❧

1939 *Birth of Dusty Springfield (Mary O'Brien), British singer*

Only choose in marriage a man whom you would choose as a friend were he a woman.

MARY FITZGERALD

❧ 17 ❧

1969 *Bernadette McAliskey (née Devlin) wins the Mid-Ulster by-election to become, at the age of 21, the youngest ever woman M.P.*

❧ 18 ❧

1829 *Birth of Mother Mary Baptist Russell, Irish nun and first Superior of the Sisters of Mercy, California*

❧ SPERANZA'S LOVE ❧

*I*n a few years such a collection would be impossible, for the old race is rapidly passing away to other lands, and in the vast working world of America with all the new influences of light and progress, the young generation, though still loving the land of their fathers, will scarcely find leisure to dream over the fairy-haunted hills and lakes and raths of ancient Ireland.

I must disclaim, however, all desire to be considered a melancholy Laudatrix temporis acti. These studies of the Irish past are simply the expression of my love for the beautiful island that gave me my first inspiration, my quickest intellectual impulses, and the strongest and best sympathies with genius and country possible to a woman's nature.

LADY FRANCESCA SPERANZA WILDE in her Preface to *Ancient Legends of Ireland*

A Summer Reverie, HENRI MARTIN (1860–1943)

⊹ **19** ⊹

You can live without your own but not without your neighbour

IRISH PROVERB

I slept and dreamed that
life was beauty,
I woke – and found that
life was duty.

ELLEN STURGIS HOOPER

⊹ **20** ⊹

Would you shackle spring to times and seasons?

AMY LOWELL

⊹ **21** ⊹

1816 *Birth of Charlotte Brontë, English novelist*

⊹ **22** ⊹

1894 *Birth of Evie Hone, Irish stained glass artist*

The Sleeping Beauty, THOMAS RALPH SPENCE (fl. 1876–1903)

❖ 23 ❖

1947 *Birth of Bernadette McAliskey (née Devlin), Irish politician and civil rights activist*

❖ 24 ❖

1961 *Birth of Laura Magahy, Irish businesswoman, best known for spearheading the development of Dublin's Temple Bar area*

❖ 25 ❖

1892 *Birth of Mother Mary Martin, Irish founder of the Medical Missionaries of Mary*

❖ 26 ❖

1979 *Grainne Cronin becomes the first woman pilot for Aer Lingus when she takes charge of the Frankfurt-Shannon flight*

Where we really love, we often dread more than we desire the solemn moment that exchanges hope for certainty.

MME DE STAËL

Day-Dreams, JEAN BEAUDUIN (1851–1916)

APRIL

❖ 27 ❖

1827 Birth of Mary Ward, Irish naturalist, artist and astronomer
1953 Death of Maud Gonne MacBride, Irish revolutionary beloved of Yeats

---
❖ 28 ❖

1875 Birth of Mother Kevin (Teresa Kearney), Irish missionary to Uganda
and founder of the Franciscan Missionary Sisters for Africa

❖ 29 ❖

Ah, 'All things come to those who wait.' They come, but often come too late.

LADY MARY M. CURRIE

❖ 30 ❖

Where is the man who has the power and skill
To stem the torrent of a woman's will?
For if she will, she will, you may depend on't;
And if she won't, she won't; so there's an end on't.

ANON.

> *So it is only by
> realising that unless
> the ideal, the spirit of self-
> sacrifice and love of country,
> is at the back of our work
> for commercial prosperity,
> sex emancipation, and other
> practical reforms, that we
> can hope to help our land.
> Every little act for Ireland's
> sake will help to build up
> a great nation, noble and
> self-sacrificing, industrious
> and free.*
>
> CONSTANCE MARKIEVICZ

I've had my soaring time,
my long, light day.

SUSAN MITCHELL

Lilies, WALTER CRANE (1845–1915)

An Irish Woman's

MAY

*I can see you young and glad
and wild,
May I never know you old
or changed.*

MARGARET MARY RYAN

MAY

 1

1891 *Opening of Dublin Loop Line railway bridge*

*N*ow and then you meet a person so exactly formed to please, that she will gain upon every one that hears or beholds her: this disposition is not merely the gift of nature, but frequently the effect of much knowledge of the world, and a command over the passions.

from *The Art of Being Agreeable* 1885

2

1943 *Birth of Margaret (Maggie) Johnston, Irish champion bowls player*
1858 *Birth of Edith Somerville, Irish writer and artist*

3

1785 *First meeting of Irish Academy*
(Royal Irish Academy from 1786)

4

1773 *Art O'Leary killed by British soldiers near Macroom, Co. Cork,*
which moved his widow Eileen to compose her famous lament

5

1942 *Birth of Tammy Wynette, American country and western singer*

6

A woman like a lamb, a quiet, friendly woman
IRISH PROVERB

7

1915 *The luxury liner Lusitania is torpedoed by a German U-boat off Kinsale, Co. Cork,*
seven days after leaving New York. Over a thousand lose their lives.
1931 *Foundation of An Óige, the Irish Youth Hostel Association*

> *Joy often comes after sorrow, like morning after night*
>
> PEGGY O'BRIEN

LEFT: *Young Friends*, LEXDEN LEWIS POCOCK (1850–1919)

$\mathcal{M}$AY

❖ 8 ❖

1883 *Birth of Mary Elizabeth (Molly) Walker – Máire Nic Shiubhlaigh – Irish republican and actress*

❖ 9 ❖

1936 *Birth of Glenda Jackson, British film actress*

❖ 10 ❖

1943 *Nineteen people killed when a 500-pound mine exploded without warning at Ballymanus Bay, Co. Donegal*

❖ 11 ❖

An inch is a great deal on a nose
IRISH PROVERB

Reflections, WALTER PLIMPTON (fl. 1865–1890)

❖ 12 ❖

1712 Building starts on Trinity College library, costing £15,000
1944 Death in Nairobi, Kenya, of Edel Mary Quinn, aged 36,
Irish Legion of Mary envoy to East Africa

❖ 13 ❖

1982 Tras Honan elected the first female Cathaoirleach of the Seanad

They say there's bread
and work for all,
And the sun shines always
there:
But I'll not forget old
Ireland,
Were it fifty times as fair.

from *The Irish Emigrant*
LADY DUFFERIN

*P*ossibly you have heard that I am, by divine indignation, a sort of author … and it is quite true. With Ireland in my heart, and epitomising something of her humour and her sufferings in my own character and story, I do trade upon the materials she furnishes me, and turning my patriotism into pounds, shillings and pence, endeavour at the same moment to serve her and support myself.

from *Florence Macarthy*
LADY SYDNEY MORGAN

❖ 14 ❖

Vanity, like murder, will out
HANNAH COWLEY

MAY

❧ 15 ❧

A woman can beat the devil

IRISH PROVERB

❧ 16 ❧

1920 *Start of three-day 'soviet' by workers at Knocklong creamery, Co. Limerick*
1955 *Birth of Olga Korbut, Russian Olympic gymnast*

❧ 17 ❧

1911 *Birth of Maureen O'Sullivan, Irish film actress*

❧ 18 ❧

1919 *Birth of Margot Fonteyn (Margaret Hookham), British prima ballerina*

❧ 19 ❧

1882 *Birth of Mary Hayden, Irish historian, campaigner for women's rights*

❧ 20 ❧

1790 *Death of Elizabeth Gunning, Duchess of Hamilton and Argyll, celebrated*
Irish beauty, so lovely that people once queued through the night to see her face

---

❧ 21 ❧

1910 *Death of Mary Anne Kelly, Irish poet 'Eva' of* The Nation *newspaper*
1944 *Birth of Mary Robinson, first woman President of Ireland*

A Pensive Mood, ROGER-JOSEPH JOURDAIN (1845–1918)

MAY

22

1864 *Birth of Mother Mary Anne Cosgrave, Irish nun and Rhodesian pioneer*
1870 *Birth of Eva Gore Booth, Irish poet, trade unionist and feminist*
1941 *Birth of Caitlín Maude, Irish poet, actress, singer and political campaigner*

23

1903 *Birth of Shelah Richards, Irish actress and director*

24

1923 *Birth of Siobhán McKenna, Irish actress*
1955 *Birth of Maura 'Soshin' O'Halloran, Irish Buddhist nun and saint*

25

1842 *Birth of Helen Blackburn, Irish pioneer of feminism, trade unionist and author*

26

1920 *Birth of Peggy Lee (Norma Egstrom), American singer*

27

1943 *Birth of Cilla Black (Priscilla White), British singer*

A HERALD OF SPRING

❖ 28 ❖

1929 *Death of Alice Stopford Green, Irish historian and author*

❖ 29 ❖

1884 *Constance Mary Lloyd married Oscar Wilde*

❖ 30 ❖

1986 *Official opening for Connacht Regional Airport at Knock, Co. Mayo,
now Horan International Airport*

❖ 31 ❖

1889 *Birth of Helen Waddell, Irish medieval scholar, poet and author*
1937 *Birth of Mary O'Rourke, Irish politician*

> *Come when you're called;*
> *And do as you're bid;*
> *Shut the door after you*
> *And you'll never be chid.*
>
> MARIA EDGEWORTH

Feeding the Ducks, LOUIS ANTOINE AUGUSTE THOMAS (fl. c. 1865)

An Irish Woman's

JUNE

*Will you stand by the seas and
behold this place
As I shall stand when you're
far away?*

MARGARET MARY RYAN

JUNE

⟡ **1** ⟡

1926 *Birth of Marilyn Monroe (Norma Jean Baker), American film actress*

⟡ **2** ⟡

1829 *Death, aged 90, of Lady Eleanor Butler, Irish recluse and one of the two celebrated 'Ladies of Llangollen'*

⟡ **3** ⟡

1878 *Birth of Sinéad Flanagan, wife of Éamon de Valera*

⟡ **4** ⟡

1864 *Birth of Ellen Lucy O'Brien (Neilí Ní Bhrian), Irish Gaelic Leaguer and ecumenist*

All through the days of childhood the garden is our fairy-ground of sweet enchantment and innocent wonder.

E.V. BOYLE

⟡ **5** ⟡

1899 *Death of Margaret Anne Cusack, the 'Nun of Kenmare', in religion Sister Mary Frances Clare, described as 'Ireland's first suffragette'*

⟡ AN IRISH BALL ⟡

The grand ball was given last Thursday, to the great contentment of the best company of both sexes. The men were gallant, the ladies were courteous! ... the musicians and singers were dressed like Arcadian shepherds and shepherdesses, and placed among the rocks. If tea, coffee or chocolate were wanting, you held your cup to a leaf of a tree, and it was filled; and whatever you wanted to eat or drink, was immediately found on a rock, or on a branch, or in the hollow of a tree. The waiters were all in whimsical dress, and every lady as she entered the room had a fine bouquet presented to her. The whole was extremely well conducted; no confusion; and the ladies say, never was there seen so enchanting a place; but a few dissenters had the assurance to say it was no better than a puppet-show.

MRS MARY DELANY
1752

LEFT: *Daydreams*, NORMAN PRESCOTT-DAVIES (1862–1915)

6

*1932 Birth of Miriam Hederman O'Brien, Irish policy consultant, broadcaster,
and a director of Allied Irish Banks*

7

1899 Birth of Elizabeth Bowen, Irish novelist and short story writer
1900 Birth of Patricia Lynch, Irish author

8

*1978 Naomi James becomes the first woman to sail solo
around the world via Cape Horn*

9

It is no secret that is known to three
IRISH PROVERB

Little deeds of kindness,
Little words of love,
Help to make earth happy
Like the heaven above.
JULIA A. FLETCHER
CARNEY

10

1922 Birth of Judy Garland (Frances Ethel Gumm), American film actress and singer

---

11

1862 Birth of Violet Florence Martin, Irish novelist who wrote under the pen name Martin Ross
1912 Birth of Mary Lavin, Irish short story writer and novelist

---

12

1929 Birth of Anne Frank, Jewish diarist

*For women there are,
undoubtedly, great
difficulties in the path, but
so much the more to
overcome. First, no woman
should say 'I am but a
woman!' But a woman!
What more can you
ask to be?*

MARIA MITCHELL

Au Bord de la Mer, François Flameng (1856–1923)

J U N E

⚜ 13 ⚜

1699 *Funeral took place of 29-year-old Molly Malone, Dublin fishmonger renowned*
as the subject of the ballad 'Cockles and Mussels'
1884 *Birth of Mary Colum, Irish writer*

⚜ 14 ⚜

An áit m-biann caint, a's an áit a m-bhiann géidh biann callán

IRISH PROVERB

⚜ 15 ⚜

1920 *Birth of Amy Clampit, American poet*

⚜ 16 ⚜

1904 *Nora Barnacle first walked out with James Joyce, and in tribute to her*
he set the action of his novel Ulysses *on this date*

⚜ 17 ⚜

1845 *Birth of Emily Lawless, Irish poet, historian and biographer*

⚜ 18 ⚜

1929 *Birth of Eva Bartok, Hungarian film actress*

⚜ 19 ⚜

1936 *Birth of Mary Holland, Irish political journalist, renowned for*
her coverage of Northern Ireland
1939 *Birth of Sister Stanislaus Kennedy, founder and president of Focus Point,*
campaigner for the homeless

❖ 20 ❖

1906 *Birth of Catherine Cookson, British novelist*
1945 *Birth of Anne Murray, Canadian singer*

❖ 21 ❖

1798 *Battle of Vinegar Hill, Enniscorthy, Co. Wexford,*
effectively the end of the 1798 Rising in Wexford

Be careful of the words
you say, keep them soft
and sweet; you never
know from day to day
which one's you'll
have to eat ....
ANON.

❖ 22 ❖

Never take a wife who has no fault
IRISH PROVERB

❖ 23 ❖

1802 *Mary O'Connell secretly marries her cousin Daniel O'Connell,*
later to be known as 'The Liberator'
1825 *Birth of Annie French Hector, Irish writer*

❖ 24 ❖

1874 *Birth of Úna Ní Fhaircheallaigh (Agnes O'Farrelly),*
Irish feminist, writer and Gaelic Leaguer

*H*ow break away? If
I was sure of
myself and knew I could
succeed for sure and make
a name or more to the
point money, I would bolt,
live on a crust and do. But
to do all that with the
chance of having to return
and throw oneself on the
charity of one's family a
miserable failure is more
than I can screw up my
courage to face. So many
people begin with great
promise…

CONSTANCE MARKIEVICZ

❖ 25 ❖

1891 *Katharine (Kitty) O'Shea married Charles Stewart Parnell*

The Flower Maiden, HENRY JOHN STOCK (1853–1930)

JUNE

⊰ **26** ⊱

1892 Birth of Pearl Buck, American author

⊰ **27** ⊱

1922 Birth of Marie Kean, Irish actress well known as Mrs Kennedy in the radio programme
The Kennedys of Castle Ross

⊰ **28** ⊱

Your success and happiness lie in you
HELEN KELLER

⊰ **29** ⊱

1820 The Dublin Society becomes the Royal Dublin Society

⊰ **30** ⊱

Falaigheann gradh gráin, agus chi fúath a lán
IRISH PROVERB

After ecstasy, the laundry.
ZEN STATEMENT

*A well-kept house is a sign
of a misspent life.*
KITCHEN PLAQUE

*A woman cannot
guarantee her heart, even
though her husband be
the greatest and most
perfect of men.*

GEORGE SAND

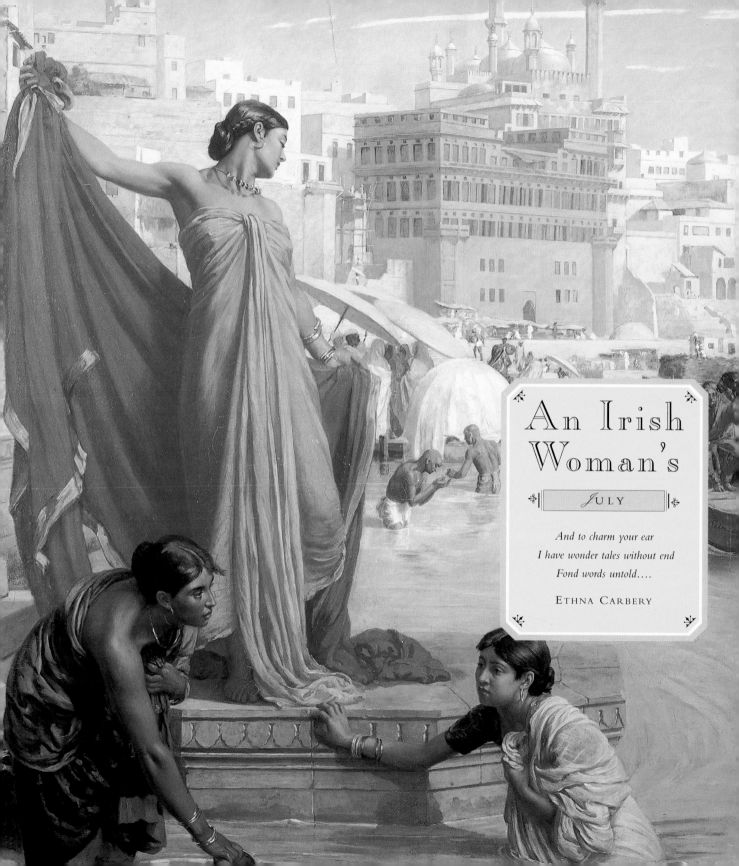

An Irish Woman's

JULY

And to charm your ear
I have wonder tales without end
Fond words untold....

ETHNA CARBERY

JULY

❧ 1 ❧

1804 *Birth of George Sand (Amandine Dupin), French novelist*
1961 *Birth of Princess Diana, former wife of the Prince of Wales*

❧ 2 ❧

1970 *Irish Catholic hierarchy announced it was no longer obligatory to
abstain from eating meat on Fridays*

❧ 3 ❧

Kiss me, kill me, love me, leave me, –
Damn me, dear, but don't deceive me!

EDITH NESBIT

❧ 4 ❧

Often was ugly amiable and pretty sulky

IRISH PROVERB

❧ 5 ❧

1958 *Birth of Veronica Guerin, Irish investigative reporter*

❧ 6 ❧

1939 *Birth of Mary Peters, Irish Olympic athlete*
1907 *Irish Crown jewels stolen and never recovered*

*Allowing children to talk incessantly is a mistake. We do not mean to say that they
should be restricted from talking in proper seasons, but they should be taught to know
when it is proper for them to cease.*

from *Golden Hints for Housewives and Home Comforts*
Magazine article c. 1913

LEFT: *Bathing in the Ganges*, VALENTINE CAMERON PRINSEP (1838–1904)

❧ 7 ❧

1739 *Death of Christian Davis, Irish female soldier, who enlisted to find her husband who had been press-ganged into the British army. She found him thirteen years later.*

❧ 8 ❧

1770 *Birth of Mary Ann McCracken, Irish patriot and philanthropist*

❧ 9 ❧

1959 *Mary Browne becomes the first Irish ban gharda (policewoman)*

> *Laziness may appear attractive, but work gives satisfaction.*
>
> MARY BARBER

❧ 10 ❧

1949 *Last-ever tram leaves from Nelson Pillar, Dublin*

*The dead who died for
      Ireland
Let not their memory die,
But solemn and bright, like
      stars at night,
Be they throned for aye
      on high.*

ELLEN O'LEARY

Summer Evening on the Skagen Southern Beach
PETER SEVERIN KROYER (1851–1909)

❧ 11 ❧

1817 *Act of Parliament establishes the first public lunatic asylums in Ireland*

❧ 12 ❧

1796 *First Orange Order 'Twelfth' demonstration was held*

❧ 13 ❧

1985 *Live Aid concert raises £45 million for Third World famine victims*

❧ 14 ❧
---

*Twenty years a-growing; twenty years at rest; twenty years declining;
and twenty years when it doesn't matter whether you're there or not.*

IRISH PROVERB

> *Mothers kept the peace
> in families. Everything
> goes back to the mother.
> It still does.*
>
> LILY FOY,
> born and bred in
> The Liberties, Dublin

The Letter, JOHN TOWNSEND (BORN 1929)

Youth's illusions, one by one
Have passed like clouds
That the sun looked on.

D.F. MACARTHY

❧ 15 ❧

1919 *Birth of Iris Murdoch, Irish philosopher and novelist*
1927 *Death of Countess Markievicz, Irish revolutionary*

❧ 16 ❧

And that my delight may be solidly fixed,
Let the friend and the lover be handsomely mixed

LADY MARY WORTLEY MONTAGU

❧ 17 ❧

1884 *Birth of Louise Gavan Duffy, Irish educator and revolutionary*

❧ 18 ❧

1951 *Fire destroys the old Abbey Theatre in Dublin*

❧ 19 ❧

Solitude is the nurse of wisdom

OLD PROVERB

❧ 20 ❧

1882 *Death of Fanny Parnell, poet and co-founder of the Ladies' Land League.*
Sister of Charles Stewart Parnell

---

*M*ighty is the force of motherhood! It transforms all things by its vital heat; it turns timidity into fierce courage, and dreadless defiance into tremulous submission; it turns thoughtfulness into foresight, and yet stills all anxiety into calm content; it makes selfishness become self-denial, and gives even to hard vanity the glance of admiring love.

from *The Mill on the Floss*, GEORGE ELIOT

The Prelude, WILLIAM WARDLAW LAING (fl. 1873–1898)

❧ 21 ❧

May the Lord keep you in his hand and never close his fist too tight on you

IRISH BLESSING

❧ 22 ❧

1860 Birth of Mother Marie Joseph Butler, Irish educator, founder of the Marymount schools and colleges in the USA and Europe

---
❧ 23 ❧

1803 Robert Emmet's uprising in Dublin begins and ends in a day

---
❧ 24 ❧

1898 Birth of Amelia Earhart, American pioneer aviator

❧ 25 ❧

The glowing ruby should adorn those who in warm July are born

ANON.

❧ 26 ❧

1914 British troops open fire on a crowd at Bachelor's Walk, Dublin, killing four and wounding 37

❧ 27 ❧

1669 Christening of Molly Malone, celebrated Irish fishmonger and subject of a ballad which became Dublin's anthem, at St Werburgh's Church

Just even to sit in a quiet church can take an awful lot off your mind.

UNA SHAW

The difference between rising every morning at six o'clock or eight, in the course of forty years, amount to 29,200 hours, or three years one hundred and twenty-one days and sixteen hours, which are equal to eight hours a day for exactly ten years. So that rising at six will be the same as if ten years of life (a weighty consideration) were added, wherein we may command eight hours every day for the cultivation of our minds and the despatch of business.

Early Rising from
ENQUIRE WITHIN UPON
EVERYTHING, 1902

❧ 28 ❧

1943 Cloghane air disaster, Co. Kerry, when ten died as a plane crashed
onto the slopes of Mount Brandon

❧ 29 ❧

Give God the praise for any well spent day

❧ 30 ❧

Women are the real architects of society
HARRIET BEECHER STOWE

❧ 31 ❧

1834 First train runs in Ireland from Dublin to Kingstown, drawn by horses
1893 Foundation of the Gaelic League to promote the Irish language

Faith is like a lily,
lifted high and white.

CHRISTINA ROSSETTI

I am the pillars of the house;
The keystone of the arch am I.
Take me away, and roof and wall
Would fall to ruin utterly.

KATHARINE TYNAN

1
1906 *Opening of Belfast City Hall*

2
1849 *Arrival in Ireland on a state visit of Queen Victoria, accompanied by Prince Albert and four children. She visited Belfast, Dublin and Cork.*

3
An ounce of mother-wit is worth a pound of clergy
SEVENTEENTH-CENTURY PROVERB

If we had no winter, the spring would not be so pleasant; if we did not sometimes taste of adversity, prosperity would not be so welcome.
ANNE BRADSTREET

4
1878 *Birth of Margaret Mary Pearse, Irish teacher, senator, sister of Patrick Pearse*

A child is the brightest ray in the sunshine of a parent's heart

TRADITIONAL
SAYING

5
1823 *Royal Hibernian Academy of Arts receives its charter*

6
1830 *Opening of the first Dublin Horse Show*

7
1943 *Death of Sarah Purser, Irish artist, portrait painter and founder, in 1903, of the acclaimed studio for stained glass 'An Túr Gloine'*
1937 *Birth of Rosemary Smith, Irish international rally driver champion*

LEFT: *Innocent Youth*, TOM MOSTYN (1864–1930)

AUGUST

So many gods, so many creeds
So many paths that wind and wind,
While just the art of being kind
Is all the sad world needs.
ELLA WILCOX

8

1879 *Birth of Eileen Gray, Irish architect and interior designer*
1953 *Opening of the Chester Beatty Library, Dublin*

9

1979 *First Vietnamese 'boat people' arrive in Ireland*

10

1976 *Peace Movement formed in Northern Ireland after the deaths of three children in Belfast*

11

A child may have too much of her mother's blessing
OLD PROVERB

MY MOTHER BIDS ME BIND MY HAIR

My mother bids me bind my hair
With bands of rosy hue,
Tie up my sleeves with ribbons rare,
And lace my bodice blue.

'For why,' she cries, 'sit still and weep,
While others dance and play?'
Alas! I scarce can go or creep
While Lubin is away.

ANNE HUNTER

GRANT

The Sweet Smell of the Rose, ARTHUR GREENBANK (fl. 1880–1900)

Love's Spell, GEORGE FREDERICK CHESTER (fl. 1861–1889)

The dove will fly
From a ruined nest,
Love will not dwell
In a troubled breast;
The heart has no zest
To sweeten life's
           dolour
If Love, the Consoler,
Be not its guest!

IRISH BALLAD

12

1821 *King George arrives in Ireland for a state visit*
in an extremely drunken condition

13

1974 *Death of Kate O'Brien, Irish novelist and dramatist*

14

One look before is better than three looks behind
IRISH PROVERB

15

1880 *Derrybeg, Co. Donegal, flooding tragedy at a chapel where*
five members of a congregation celebrating mass were drowned

16

1711 *Opening of the medical school, laboratory and anatomical*
theatre at Trinity College Dublin

17

1734 *Ten-bed hospital opened by Mary Mercer in Dublin*
1921 *Birth of Maureen O'Hara (Maureen Fitzsimmons), Irish film actress*

18

Backward, turn backward, O Time in thy flight;
Make me a child again, just for tonight
ELIZABETH AKERS ALLEN

What do I want of thee?
No gift of smile or tear
Nor casual company,
But in still speech to me
Only thy heart to hear.

SUSAN MITCHELL

❧ 19 ❧
1883 *Birth of Coco Chanel (Gabriella Chanel), French fashion designer*

> *We never know how*
> *high we are*
> *Till we are called to rise;*
> *And then, if we are true*
> *to plan,*
> *Our statures touch*
> *the skies.*
>
> EMILY DICKINSON

❧ 20 ❧
If you want to know me, come and live with me
IRISH PROVERB

❧ 21 ❧
1854 *Last ever Donnybrook Fair*
1879 *Apparitions at Knock, Co. Mayo of the Virgin Mary seen by*
at least 22 people over two hours

❧ 22 ❧
1893 *Birth of Dorothy Parker, American author and wit*

❧ 23 ❧
Do you remember yet, a gradh, the sunshine of that day…?
ETHNA CARBERY

❧ 24 ❧

> *He used to say, 'Mother, if I ever win anything on the horses I'll bring you a gramophone'. Well, here one day me mother … sees the door opening and a big horn, and him carrying the thing. He was after winning £3.10. And bought the gramophone, His Master's Voice. Big, big green thing. Oh, we were charmed…. Me mother, she had brown eyes and they nearly fell out of her head. And she kept kissing him. The whole £3.10! On her. That's all he wanted. He idolised her.*
>
> MARY DOOLAN, *former Dublin tenement resident*

The Kiosk, FRANCIS JOHN WYBURD (fl. 1846–1893)

AUGUST

✣ 25 ✣

Read not books alone, but men; and above all, read thyself

VICTORIAN SAYING

✣ 26 ✣

1913 *First day of the Great 'Lock-Out' in Dublin. By the end of September, 100,000 Dubliners faced starvation.*

✣ 27 ✣

1910 *Birth of Mother Theresa of Calcutta, Yugoslavian nun*

*At Clitheroe through the
sunset hour
My soul was very far away:
I saw Ben Bulben's rose
and fire
Shining afar o'er Sligo Bay.*

EVA GORE-BOOTH

✣ 28 ✣

1815 *Birth of Mary Martin, Irish novelist*
1929 *Birth of Jackie Onassis, widow of President Kennedy*

✣ 29 ✣

1750 *Death of Laetitia Pilkington, Irish writer and adventurer*
1890 *Opening of the National Library of Ireland*

✣ 30 ✣

1841 *First published edition of* The Cork Examiner
1951 *Birth of Dana (Rosemary Brown), Irish singer*

✣ 31 ✣

*Wear a sardonyx or for thee
No conjugal felicity.
The August-born without this stone
'Tis said must live unloved and lone.*

ANON.

An excellent medicine is brimstone and treacle, prepared by mixing an ounce and a half of sulphur, and half-an-ounce of cream of tartar, with eight ounces of treacle; and, according to the age of the child, giving from a small teaspoonful to a dessertspoonful early in the morning, two or three times a week....

'Summer Aperients for Children' from
ENQUIRE WITHIN UPON EVERYTHING, 1911

Comparing Cards, ANONYMOUS (19/20TH CENTURY)

An Irish Woman's

✦ SEPTEMBER ✦

Rise from your knees, O
daughters, rise!
Our mother still is young and fair,
Let the world look into your eyes
And see her beauty shining there.

from *To the Daughters of Erin*
SUSAN MITCHELL

⚜ 1 ⚜

1737 *First edition of* The Belfast Newsletter, *Ireland's oldest daily newspaper*
1789 *Birth of Marguerite, Countess of Blessington, Irish novelist, beauty and gossip writer*
1830 *The Zoological Gardens, Dublin, the third oldest in the world, opened to the public*

⚜ 2 ⚜

To meet, worth parting for:

Bitter forgot in sweet.

CHRISTINA ROSSETTI

> *No entertainment is so cheap as reading, nor any pleasure so lasting.*
>
> LADY MARY
> WORTLEY MONTAGU

⚜ 3 ⚜

1850 *Establishment of Queen's Colleges in Belfast, Cork and Galway, now
Queen's University, University College Cork and University College Galway*

⚜ 4 ⚜

1935 *Birth of Pauline Bewick, Irish artist*
1989 *Century Radio, Ireland's first national commercial station, goes on the air*

> *Of all the systems which human nature in its moments of intoxication has produced — if indeed a bundle of contradictions and absurdities may be called a system — that which men have contrived with a view to forming the minds, and regulating the conduct of women, is perhaps the most completely absurd.*
>
> MARY HAYS
> 1798

⚜ 5 ⚜

1911 *Formation of the Irish Women Workers' Union*
1958 *Birth of Kathy Prendergast, Irish artist*

⚜ 6 ⚜

1911 *Birth of Lady Angela Christina McDonnell Antrim,
Irish sculptor and cartoonist*

⚜ 7 ⚜

1984 *Restoration of the Royal Hospital, Kilmainham, completed*

LEFT: *Le Rendez-vouz,* HARRY JOHN PEARSON (1872–1933)

SEPTEMBER

How much more miserable we should be than we are if we had our eyes opened to discern always true from make-believe.

GERALDINE JEWSBURY

8

1908 *St Enda's School opens under the headmastership of Patrick Pearse*

9

1649 *Siege of Drogheda, by Oliver Cromwell's army, begins*

10

1813 *Fall of Ireland's largest meteorite, the 'Limerick Stone' of 65 pounds*

11

There is no cure for love but marriage
IRISH PROVERB

Finished 'Work', — twenty chapters. Not what it should be — too many interruptions. Should like to do one book in peace, and see if it wouldn't be good.

LOUISA MAY ALCOTT
1872

Letter, with Quill Pen, ADOLPHE PIOT (c. 1890)

The Annunciation, EDWARD REGINALD FRAMPTON (1872–1923)

Love her, do not leave her,
O'er the world to roam;
Ireland needs her children:
Work for her at home!

GAELIC LEAGUE

✦ 12 ✦

It is one of the privileges of friendship to talk of our own follies and infirmities
LADY MARY WORTLEY MONTAGU

✦ 13 ✦

1845 Gardener's Chronicle and Horticultural Gazette *stops the presses to report the failure of the potato crop*

✦ 14 ✦

1866 *Birth of Alice Milligan, Irish writer, nationalist and Irish revivalist*
1907 *Birth of Edel Quinn, Irish Legion of Mary envoy to East Africa*

❧ 15 ❧

*1976 Mrs Anne Dickson becomes the first woman to lead an Irish political party,
the Unionist Party of Northern Ireland*
1974 Death of Mrs Sydney Czira, née Sydney Gifford, Republican journalist

❧ 16 ❧

Bionn an grádh caoch

IRISH PROVERB

❧ 17 ❧

1934 Birth of Maureen Connolly (Little Mo), Irish-American tennis champion

Prison. It was not prison for me. Hungerstrikes. They had no fears for me. Cat and Mouse Act. I could have laughed. A prison cell was quiet — no telephone, no paper, no speeches, no sea sickness, no sleepless nights. I could lie on my plank bed all day and all night and return once more to my daydreams.

ANNIE KENNEY
Suffragette

❧ 18 ❧

*1851 Death of Anne Devlin, Irish patriot and heroine, a committed rebel referred to as 'Robert
Emmet's housekeeper' by historians*

❧ 19 ❧

1757 Opening of St Patrick's Hospital, Dublin, an asylum for the mentally ill

At twenty my complexion was like alabaster, and at five paces distant the sharpest eyes could not discover my pearl necklace from my skin.

LADY HESTER
STANHOPE

❧ 20 ❧

1588 Three ships of the Spanish Armada run aground at Streedagh, Co. Sligo
1896 Birth of Norah Hoult, Irish writer

❧ 21 ❧

*Thou straggler into loving arms,
Young climber-up of knees,
When I forget thy thousand ways
Then life and all shall cease.*

MARY LAMB

La Primavera, detail of the Three Graces, SANDRO BOTTICELLI (1445–1510)

SEPTEMBER

⋇ 22 ⋇

1884 *HMS Wasp was wrecked off Tory Island with the loss of 52 lives*

⋇ 23 ⋇

To the whole world my tenderness be known
What is the world to her, who lives for thee alone.
MARTHA SANSOM

⋇ 24 ⋇

1861 *Opening of Mater Hospital, Dublin*
1944 *Birth of Eavan Boland, Irish poet*

⋇ 25 ⋇

Better good manners than good looks
IRISH PROVERB

The clouds had made a crimson
crown
Above the mountains high.
The stormy sun was going
down
In a stormy sky.

Why did you let your eyes so
rest on me
And hold your breath between?
In all the ages this can never be
As if it had not been.

⋇ 26 ⋇

1766 *Death of Frances Sheridan (née Chamberlaine), novelist, playwright and mother of Richard Brinsley Sheridan*
1873 *Birth of Anna Smithson, Irish novelist and nurse*

A Moment
MARY ELIZABETH
COLERIDGE

⋇ 27 ⋇

1972 *Opening of the National Institute for Higher Education, Limerick, now the University of Limerick*

SEPTEMBER

⚜ 28 ⚜

1912 *Ulster's Solemn League and Covenant was signed in Belfast by 237,368 men against Home Rule; 234,046 women signed a parallel declaration*

⚜ 29 ⚜

1778 *Birth of Catherine McAuley, Irish founder of the Order of Mercy*
1908 *Birth of Greer Garson, Academy-Award-winning Irish film actress*

⚜ 30 ⚜

1959 *World premiere of* Mise Eire *at Cork Film Festival*

My dreams were all my own; I accounted for them to nobody; they were my refuge when annoyed, my dearest pleasure when free.

MARY SHELLEY

*B*ut no matter how poor they'd be on a Saturday night they'd be sitting outside. People'd all come around and sit on the steps and they'd get pig's legs or a pig's cheek or ribs and they shared it. Shared everything with one another. Same with births, deaths, and marriage, they all came. Everybody helped. Children would be out playing and the parents would be together. And we used to have a lot of street singers. There was a woman used to play the banjo and she'd come along and sing and there was a girl that'd play the violin and she was great …
just to sit and listen to her.

ELIZABETH 'BLUEBELL' MURPHY
former resident of a tenement on Corporation Street, Dublin

Elaine from la Mort d'Arthur, CHARLES EDWIN FRIPP (1854–1906)

An Irish Woman's

OCTOBER

'Twas the dream of a God
And the mould of his hand,
That you shook 'neath His stroke,
That you trembled and broke
To this beautiful land.

Ireland
DORA SIGERSON
SHORTER

OCTOBER

1
1911 *Unveiling of the Parnell Monument in O'Connell Street, Dublin*

2
1942 *The cruiser* Curaçao *sinks off the Co. Donegal coast with the loss of 338 lives
after colliding with the liner* Queen Mary

3
1980 *Miss Justice Mella Carroll becomes the first female judge of the Irish High Court*

4
Mairg ná deineann cómhairle deaghmhná
IRISH PROVERB

5
1968 *Northern Ireland Civil Rights Association march in Derry*

6
1928 *Birth of Maeve Kyle, international athlete and hockey player*

*To live happily, try to
promote the happiness
of others.*

Advice to Young Ladies
Magazine article, c. 1911

7
*Greatly shining,
The Autumn moon floats in the thin sky …*
AMY LOWELL

LEFT: *The Tryst*, WILLIAM HOLYOAKE (1834–1894)

OCTOBER

8

1858 *Birth of Edith Somerville, Irish novelist*

9

1891 *Birth of Lil Nic Dhonnachachadha (Lilian Duncan)*
teacher and Irish language worker

10

1977 *Mairead Corrigan and Betty Williams, founders of the Peace Movement in Northern*
Ireland, win the Nobel Prize for Peace

11

1866 *Opening of Alexandra College for girls, Dublin*
1973 *Mary Tinney, Ireland's first woman ambassador, appointed to Sweden and Finland*

12

1969 *Death of Louise Gavan Duffy, pioneering educationalist; one of the first women to enter*
UCD and founder of Scoil Bhríde, the first all-Irish school for girls, Dublin, 1917

13

1981 *Publication of the first Irish-language version of the Bible for over 200 years*

14

1917 *Magdalen Hone, widow of Nathaniel Hone the artist, presents 500 of his oil paintings*
and 900 watercolours to the National Gallery of Ireland

Shall mine eyes behold thy
glory, O my country?
FANNY PARNELL

Carrying the Peacock, JOHN DAWSON WATSON (1832–1892)

✢ 15 ✢

1889 *Birth of Margaret Burke Sheridan ('Divine Diva'), Irish soprano*

> *If effect be the best proof of eloquence, then mine was a good speech.*
>
> HANNAH MORE

✢ 16 ✢

A foster child is as he is brought up

IRISH PROVERB

✢ 17 ✢

1907 *Marconi telegraphy service starts between Clifden, Co. Galway, and Cape Breton, Canada*

✢ 18 ✢
---

c. 1780 *Birth of Peg Woffington, Irish actress*

✢ 19 ✢

1913 *Death of Emily Lawless, Irish novelist and poet*

✢ 20 ✢
---

*Up, maiden fair! and bind thy hair,
And rouse thee in the breezy air.*

JOANNA BAILLIE

OCTOBER

❧ 21 ❧

1917 *George Hyde-Lees, aged 26, marries the poet W. B. Yeats, aged 52*
1951 *First Wexford Opera Festival takes place*

❧ 22 ❧

1884 *First women graduates conferred by the Royal University of Ireland*

❧ 23 ❧

Whoso loves believes the impossible
ELIZABETH BARRETT BROWNING

The family was very powerful, you know, very comforting. And the extended family with the grannies. The granny was the matriarch. She minded the children and told everybody what to do. She was very powerful and much loved. The fathers never worked. Never worked. Whatever income was coming in was gained by the mothers …

PEGGY PIGOTT,
Northside Dublin
teacher in the 1950s

❧ 24 ❧

1880 *First meeting of the Irish Ladies' Land League, founded by Fanny Parnell, Jane Byrne and Ellen Ford in New York*

❧ 25 ❧

1968 *New University of Coleraine, Ulster, officially opens*

*Come the wind may
never again
Blow as it blows now
for us …*

EMILY BRONTË

❧ 26 ❧

Love me still but know not why, so hast thou the same reason still to dote upon me ever.
ANON.

❧ 27 ❧

1932 *Birth of Sylvia Plath, American poet and novelist*

When Sorrow Comes in Summer Days, Roses Bloom in Vain
JOHN MELHUISH STRUDWICK (1849–1937)

OCTOBER

28

1927 *Cleggan Disaster, when 16 fishermen drown off the coast of Galway, nine from Inishbofin*

---

*Western wind, when will
thou blow
The small rain down can
rain?
Christ, if my love were
in my arms
And I in my bed again!*

ANONYMOUS
16th century

29

1825 *Birth of Catherine Hayes, Irish opera singer known as the 'Irish Nightingale'*

30

1865 *Birth of Rose Mabel Young, Irish Gaelic scholar*

31

1883 *Birth of Sarah Allgood, Irish actress*

*W*e recommend our
readers attain
perfection in this branch of
fancy work, because, above
all others, it is a resource to
those who, from weak eyes,
are precluded from many
forms of industrial
amusement, or who, as
invalids, cannot bear the
fatigue of more elaborate
work. The fact is that
knitting does not require
eyesight at all; and a very
little practice ought to
enable any one to knit
whilst reading, talking, or
studying, quite as well as if
the fingers were
unemployed.

'Knitting Explained'
Edwardian article

An Irish Woman's

NOVEMBER

No art I used men's love to draw;
I lived but by my being's law,
As roses are by heaven designed
To bring the honey to the wind.

KATHERINE BRADLEY
& EDITH COOPER

*N*OVEMBER

1
Tástáil do dhuine muinteartha sul a dteastóidh sé uait
IRISH PROVERB

2
1952 *Death of Molly Allgood, Irish actress*

3
1969 *Breathalyser introduced into the Republic*

4
1974 *Powerscourt House, Enniskerry, Co. Wicklow, destroyed by fire*

5
1850 *Birth of Ella Wheeler Wilcox, American feminist activist*

6
Mankind should hope, in wedlock's state,
A friend to find as well as mate …
MARY SAVAGE

7
1878 *Birth of Margaret Cousins (née Gillespie), Irish teacher and worker*
for women's rights in India
1968 *Senator Margaret Pearse accorded a state funeral*

> *I*n France or Italy …
> women, in losing one
> virtue, are not necessarily
> exposed to the loss of all.
> There our sex are saved from
> the necessity of hypocrisy;
> and are not compelled to pull
> down the reputations of their
> contemporaries, in order to
> erect on the ruins a pedestal
> for the elevation of their own.
>
> MARGUERITE, COUNTESS
> OF BLESSINGTON
> 1837

> *Men of Sense in all Ages*
> *abhor those customs*
> *which treat us only as*
> *the vassals of your Sex.*
>
> ABIGAIL ADAMS

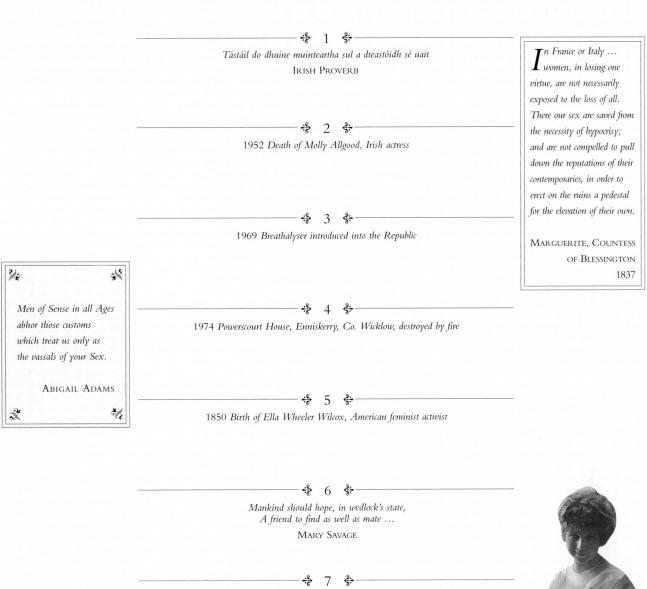

LEFT: *An Afternoon Ride in Hyde Park, London,* A.F. DE PRADES (fl. 1862–1879)

⁖ 8 ⁖

1900 *Birth of Margaret Mitchell, American writer*

⁖ 9 ⁖

1935 *Arranmore, Co. Donegal, boating tragedy, when 19 drown off Arranmore Island, 12 of these being islanders returning from a potato harvest in Scotland*

> *O'er this marble drop a tear,*
> *Here lies fair Rosalinde;*
> *All mankind was pleased with her,*
> *And she with all mankind.*
>
> *A Gallant Lady's Epitaph*
> MRS MONK

⁖ 10 ⁖

1896 *Birth of Lady Mary Heath, record-breaking Irish pioneer aviator and athlete*

⁖ 11 ⁖

1908 *Irish Women's Franchise League founded by Hanna Sheehy-Skeffington and Margaret Cousins*

⁖ 12 ⁖

1929 *Birth of Grace Kelly, Irish-American film actress and later Princess of Monaco*
1967 *First Rosc Art Exhibition at the Royal Dublin Society's H.Q., Ballsbridge, Dublin*

⁖ SWEET WICKLOW MOUNTAINS ⁖

Sweet Wicklow mountains! the sunlight sleeping
On your green banks is a picture rare,
You crowd around me, like young girls peeping,
And puzzling me to say which is most fair;
As tho' you'd see your own sweet faces,
Reflected in that smooth and silver sea,
Oh! my blessin' on those lovely places,
Tho' no one cares how dear they are to me.

from *Oh! Bay of Dublin*
LADY DUFFERIN

WILLS'S CIGARETTES.

13

1831 *Sisters of Mercy established by Catherine McAuley*
1863 *St Stephen's Green open to the public*

14

Beauty is the possession of him to whom it is born, but it is manner that captivates every one

IRISH PROVERB

LAMBERT & BUTLER'S CIGARETTES. LADIES SKI-ING.

15

1887 *Birth of Georgia O'Keefe, American artist*

16

1986 *Death of Siobhán McKenna, Irish actress*

> *Dread remorse when you are tempted to err, Miss Eyre: remorse is the poison of life.*
>
> CHARLOTTE BRONTË

17

1930 *First Irish Hospital Sweepstakes draw sees first prize of $208,792 shared between three winners*

18

1967 *Sculpture of Wolfe Tone unveiled at St Stephen's Green, Dublin*

19

1871 *Birth of Margaret Dobbs, Irish historian and Gaelic Leaguer*
1900 *Birth of Pamela Hinkson, Irish writer and daughter of Katharine Tynan*

Humanity is like a bird with its two wings – the one is male, the other female. Unless both wings are strong and impelled by some common force, the bird cannot fly heavenwards. According to the spirit of this age, women must advance and fulfil their mission in all departments of life, becoming equal to men. They must be on the same level as men and enjoy equal rights.

'ABDU'L BAHÁ

❧ 20 ❧

1969 *Death of Josephine MacNeill, first Irish woman diplomatic representative abroad*

❧ 21 ❧

Tógh do chuideachta sul a suidhfir
IRISH PROVERB

> *She had a womanly instinct that clothes possess an influence more powerful over many than the worth of character or the magic of manners.*
>
> LOUISA MAY ALCOTT

❧ 22 ❧

1919 *Birth of Máire Drumm, Irish republican*

❧ 23 ❧

1819 *Birth of Margaret Aylward, Irish founder of the Sisters of the Holy Faith*
1845 *Birth of Charlotte O'Brien, Irish social reformer, botanist and writer*

ℕ OVEMBER

❧ 24 ☙

Success is counted sweetest
By those who ne'er succeed

EMILY DICKINSON

❧ 25 ☙

1906 *Birth of Saidie Paterson, Irish trade unionist and peace activist*

❧ 26 ☙

1794 *First Irish transported convicts arrive in New South Wales, Australia*

❧ 27 ☙

1871 *Gaiety Theatre, Dublin, opens with a production of* She Stoops to Conquer

Beyond, beyond the
mountain line,
The greystone and the
boulder,
Beyond the growth of dark
green pine,
That crowns its western
shoulder,
There lies that fairy land of
mine,
Unseen of a beholder.

from *Dreams*
MRS ALEXANDER

Give me a generous soul
that glows
With other's transports,
other's woes …

ELIZABETH RYVES

NOVEMBER

❧ 28 ❧

Nothing is preferable to reconciliation
IRISH PROVERB

❧ 29 ❧

1832 *Birth of Louisa May Alcott, American author*

*My love in her attire doth
show her wit,
It doth so well become her.*
ANON.

❧ 30 ❧

1969 *Birth of Catherina McKiernan, champion Irish cross-country athlete*

Dressing from twelve to three. Madame Tornure sent me a most unbecoming cap: mem. I shall leave her off when I have paid her bill. Heigh-ho! when will that be? Tormented by duns, jewellers, mercers, milliners: I think they always fix on Mondays for dunning: I suppose it is because they know one is sure to be horribly vapored after a Sunday-evening's party, and they like to increase one's miseries.

from *Journal of a Lady of Fashion*
MARGUERITE, COUNTESS OF BLESSINGTON

Romantic Thoughts, WALTER ANDERSON (fl. 1856–1886)

An Irish Woman's

I cannot sing the old songs
I sang long years ago,
For heart and voice would fail me
And foolish tears would flow.

CHARLOTTE BARNARD

DECEMBER

❧ 1 ❧

1722 *Death of Susanna Centlivre, Irish playwright*

*My impression is
deepening every day that
Ireland is as much a
foreign country to England
as is France or Italy.*

LADY ELIZABETH
BUTLER

❧ 2 ❧

1811 *Kildare Place Society founded to organise non-denominational schools in Ireland*

❧ 3 ❧

1897 *Birth of Kate O'Brien, Irish author and playwright*
1990 *Mary Robinson installed as seventh President of Ireland*

❧ 4 ❧

1822 *Birth of Frances Power Cobbe, Irish essayist*
1887 *Birth of Winifred Carney, Irish socialist, trade unionist and revolutionary*

❧ 5 ❧

1830 *Birth of Christina Rossetti, English poet*

❧ ELLEN O'LEARY ❧

She had grown old waiting for this little time of union with the brother who fulfilled her sternest ideals. Once she told me she had never been in love because she had never met a man like her brother. One could believe it, for there was something virginal about her, as if she had never known the little softness and folly of love ... Yet with true love she had keen sympathy. One would not bare to her for worlds one's little follies and fancies, the vagrant preferences, the indiscretions, that most girls and women know of themselves and others. Love, with her, to be believed in, must have had more than an element of loftiness.... I have never known a woman so strong.

KATHARINE TYNAN
writing about her memory of Ellen O'Leary in *'An Exile's Sister'*

DECEMBER

⦿ 6 ⦿

1920 *Birth of Elizabeth (Lizzie) Crotty, Irish traditional musician*
1922 *Irish Free State comes into existence*

⦿ 7 ⦿

Short and sweet like an ass's trot
TRADITIONAL PROVERB

⦿ 8 ⦿

1542 *Birth of Mary Queen of Scots*

⦿ 9 ⦿

1969 *The National Gallery of Ireland purchases Goya's 'The Dream' for £145,000*

⦿ 10 ⦿

1830 *Birth of Emily Dickinson, American poet*

---

*Not in vain is Ireland
pouring itself all over the
earth … The Irish, with
their glowing hearts and
reverent credulity, are
needed in this cold age of
intellect and scepticism.*

LYDIA CHILD

⦿ 11 ⦿

*Oh my son's my son till he gets him a wife,
But my daughter's my daughter all her life.*
DINAH CRAIK

⦿ 12 ⦿

1873 *Birth of Lola Ridge, Irish poet and radical*
1928 *Issue of the new Free State currency*

---

*She was then but
fourteen but her size
forced her to dress quite
Womanly—She led us into
a new Species of Culinary
Preparations—Namely
making up washes and
beautifying lotions—We had
two or three of the Tenants
every day hunting the
Country for different sorts
of Herbs, and such Plaisters
and Milk Washes as We
made up would be enough
to ruin all the fair Skins in
the Circassioan Marts—
Every night we were wrapd
up like Pomatum Sticks in
greasy brown Paper, and
I'm sure if any Stranger
had seen us at Night they
would have taken [us] for
three Egyptian Mummies
ready Embalmd.*

from *Retrospections
of an Outcast*
DOROTHEA HERBERT

In the Park, George Dunlop Leslie (1835–1921)

 13

*1945 Family Allowances Act (NI) provides for payment of 5s per week for
second and subsequent children*
1952 Adoption Act (RI) stipulates that adopters must be of the same religion as the adopted child

---

 14

1874 Death of Biddy Early, Irish white witch

 15

1930 Birth of Edna O'Brien, Irish novelist

 16

*1911 Local Authorities (Ireland) (Qualification of Women) Act allows
women to become members of county and borough councils*

 17

*1834 First railway in Ireland and the world's first suburban railway from Dublin to Kingstown
(Dun Laoghaire) was opened*

 18

Cha robh se air faghail, 'n úair a bhi an chiall da roinn
IRISH PROVERB

 19

1973 Irish Supreme Court rules against the prohibition of the importation of contraceptives

---

*There is nothing so
strong as the force of
love; there is no love so
forcible as the love of an
affectionate mother to her
natural child.*

ELIZABETH
GRYMESTON

---

*O ne might say I had
had already a
sufficiently large share of the
earth's beauties to enjoy, yet
here opened out an utterly
new and unique experience
– Ireland. Our wedding
tour was chiefly devoted to
the Wild West, with a
pause at Glencar, in Kerry.
I have tried … to convey to
my readers … my
impression of that Western
country – its freshness, its
wild beauty, its entrancing
poetry, and that sadness
which, like the minor key
in music, is the most
appealing quality in poetry.
… My husband had given
me the choice of a locale for
the wedding tour between
Ireland and the Crimea.
How could I hesitate?*

*from A Soldier's Wife, an
Autobiography*
LADY ELIZABETH BUTLER

DECEMBER

⊰ 20 ⊱

1909 *Ireland's first cinema, The Volta, opens in Mary St, Dublin*

⊰ 21 ⊱

1915 *Death of Violet Martin, Irish novelist under the pen-name of Martin Ross*
1985 *Foundation of the Progressive Democratic Party*

⊰ 22 ⊱

Christmas when I was young … ah, it was grand.
PEGGY FITZGERALD

⊰ 23 ⊱

1834 *Last reported sighting of Great Auk in Ireland, off Waterford Harbour*
1899 *Birth of Máiréad Ní Ghráda, Irish playwright and author*
1958 *Death of Dorothy Macardle, Irish historian*

⊰ 24 ⊱

1946 *Departments of Health and Social Welfare established in the Republic*

> *Old Scotia's jocund*
> Highland reel
> *Might make a hermit play*
> *the deel!*
> *So full of jig!*
> *Famed for its Cortillons*
> *gay France is*
> *But e'en give me the dance*
> *of dances*
> *An Irish jig.*
>
> LADY MORGAN

⊰ YESTERDAY'S CHRISTMAS ⊱

*Y*ou got your Christmas candle, always red, for nothing where you brought your groceries. And the man at the dairy across the road where we used to get our milk and butter, well, he always gave us a goose for Christmas. And everybody made Christmas pudding. Each week you'd spend a few bob and put it by until you got all the ingredients. You'd start collecting raisins and currants and the cinnamon and the nutmeg and spice. Then you'd get a big calico cloth and you'd grease it first with butter – or margarine – and then put it all in and tie it and boil that for about six or seven hours. Then leave it hanging for a few days and it would be so beautiful.

ELIZABETH 'BLUEBELL' MURPHY

DECEMBER

✤ 25 ✤
Christmas Day

✤ 26 ✤
1916 *Birth of Kathleen O'Flaherty, Irish academic and author*

Brief, on a flying night
From the shaken tower,
A flock of bells take flight,
And go with the hour.

Like birds from the cote to
*   the gales,*
Abrupt − O hark!
A fleet of bells set sails,
And go into the dark.

✤ 27 ✤
1904 *Opening of the Abbey Theatre in Dublin with a double bill,* On Baile's Strand
by W.B. Yeats and Spreading the News *by Lady Gregory*

Sudden the cold airs swing,
Alone, aloud,
A verse of bells takes wing
And flies with the cloud.

Chimes
ALICE MEYNALL

✤ 28 ✤
It is not an invitation without a drink
IRISH PROVERB

Today shall be as
yesterday,
The red blood burns in
Ireland still.

SUSAN MITCHELL

✤ 29 ✤
1932 *Birth of Eileen Desmond, Irish MP and Minister of Health and Social Welfare, 1981-2*

✤ 30 ✤
Conversation is a cure for every sorrow
TRADITIONAL SAYING

✤ 31 ✤
1820 *Birth of Mary Ann Sadlier, Irish novelist, businesswoman and publisher*

A Symphony, JOHN MELHUISH STRUDWICK (1849–1937)